POCAHONTAS

"**W**here is Pocahontas?" asked Chief Powhatan. Everyone in the village had turned out to welcome home their leader and his brave warriors — everyone, that is, except Powhatan's beloved daughter, Pocahontas.

As usual, Pocahontas was off on an adventure with her two friends, Meeko the raccoon, and a hummingbird called Flit. But she rushed home when she heard her father had returned. She wanted to tell him about a dream she kept having in which she saw a spinning arrow. She knew it meant something exciting was going to happen. But what?

When she finally met with her father and told him about the dream, he said, "Something exciting *is* about to happen. Kocoum has asked to seek your hand in marriage." Then he gave her a necklace, the same one her mother had worn at her wedding.

The problem was, Pocahontas did not want to marry Kocoum. He never smiled. And besides, she had a feeling her dream was pointing her down another path.

So she went to see Grandmother Willow for advice.

"All around you are spirits, child," the wise tree spirit said. "They live in the earth, the water, the sky. If you listen, they will guide you."

Just then, a breeze began to blow. Pocahontas ran to the shore and climbed a cliff, hoping to hear what the wind was telling her.

That's when she saw something she had never seen before. It was the *Susan Constant*, its sails flapping in the breeze. The ship had sailed all the way from England, bringing settlers to the land where Pocahontas lived.

The first one off the ship was John Smith. He was eager to explore this new land.

Meeko was just as eager to investigate the stranger. And when Smith gave Meeko a biscuit, the raccoon was so excited that he nearly gave away Pocahontas's hiding place. But just then, a bugle sounded, calling Smith back to his companions.

Smith had to attend a ceremony, and watch
Governor Ratcliffe plant the British flag.
Ratcliffe said he was claiming the new land for
his king and country. But all he really cared
about was the gold he hoped to find.

Ratcliffe sent John Smith to scout for Indians. Then he readied his cannons. The greedy governor was not about to let anyone get in his way.

Meanwhile, a party of warriors had spotted the settlers. When they reported this to their chief, Powhatan asked the village medicine man to find out what their arrival meant.

The medicine man threw some powder on the fire. The smoke that rose from the flames took the shape of hungry wolves, and of soldiers with weapons that spouted fire.

"Take some men to the river to observe these visitors," Powhatan told Kocoum. "Let us hope they do not intend to stay."

John Smith was scouting in the forest, when he sensed that he was not alone. Turning, he saw Pocahontas through the mist of a waterfall. They stared at each other for a long moment, before Pocahontas darted away.

"No, wait, please..." Smith called after her.

Then Pocahontas remembered what Grandmother Willow had said — to listen with her heart to the voices around her. So she decided to stop and listen to this stranger.

As they got to know each other, Pocahontas realized that Smith had some odd ideas. For instance, he thought the Indians were savages. And he did not understand that all the parts of nature — people, animals, plants, even the wind and clouds — were alive, and connected to each other.

So she showed John Smith her world. Slowly, he started to see the colors and shapes of the wind, and the rest of nature, just as she did. When they parted at the end of the day, neither one wanted to say good-bye.

Soon the tension between the settlers and Indians began to worsen. Ratcliffe had found no gold, and was furious. He was sure the Indians were hiding it all.

One of the Indian warriors who had gone to observe the settlers with Kocoum had been shot and wounded. Powhatan gave orders that no one was to go near the settlers.

But Pocahontas ignored his order. She even ignored the warning of her best friend, Nakoma, who told her to stay away from John Smith. Instead, Pocahontas led Smith to Grandmother Willow's glade where they could talk in peace.

That's when she found out that the settlers had come for gold. Pocahontas told Smith that the only gold the Indians had was the golden corn they grew in their fields.

They were still talking, when Grandmother Willow joined the conversation. "That tree is talking to me," Smith said, shaken.

"Don't be frightened," the tree spirit told him. "My bark is worse than my bite." Soon, Grandmother Willow and John Smith were chatting like old friends. Pocahontas was pleased that Grandmother Willow approved of her new friend.

But suddenly, they were interrupted by the shouts of two settlers who were looking for Smith.

Smith left, and Pocahontas hurried home. Remembering how kind and understanding Smith had been, she went to her father and begged him to talk to the settlers, instead of fighting. "It's not that simple," Powhatan replied.

At the settlement, Smith tried to explain that the Indians had no gold, but that they would share their corn which they used as food. Ratcliffe ignored him. "This is my land!" he cried.

That night, Smith and Pocahontas secretly met again to try to discuss how to keep the peace between their peoples.

But Nakoma, worried for her friend's safety, told Kocoum where Pocahontas had gone. When Kocoum found Pocahontas in the arms of Smith, he attacked.

Smith's friend Thomas arrived just in time to see Kocoum with a knife raised against Smith. He fired his musket, killing Kocoum.

"Thomas, get out of here!" Smith yelled. Thomas ran back to the settlement, but when a party of warriors appeared moments later, they accused Smith of the murder, and dragged him away.

Powhatan condemned Smith to die at sunrise. And he had harsh words for Pocahontas. "Because of your foolishness, Kocoum is dead. You have shamed your father!" he said.

Ratcliffe was equally furious when he learned
that the Indians had captured Smith. He
decided to use this information to lead the
settlers into battle against the Indians.

Meanwhile, Pocahontas was holding Smith's
compass, which Smith had given to little
Meeko. When the compass arrow began
spinning wildly, Pocahontas realized it was the
arrow from her dream.
Suddenly the arrow
stopped and pointed
toward the sunrise
. . . and John
Smith. Pocahontas
began to run in the
direction the arrow was
pointing.

Just before sunrise, the Indians arrived at the place of execution. The settlers were also marching, armed and angry, to the same spot. It seemed that nothing could prevent bloodshed now.

Then, just as Powhatan raised a huge club over Smith, Pocahontas appeared.

She threw herself over Smith and shouted, "No! If you kill him, you'll have to kill me too! Look around you. This is where the path of hatred has brought us."

No one moved. Then Pocahontas said, "You have the power to change that, Father."

Powhatan heard the wisdom of his daughter's words. He announced that there would be no more killing. "Let us be guided instead to a place of peace," he said.

When the Indian warriors put down their weapons, Ratcliffe yelled, "Now's our chance, men. Fire!" But the settlers had finally understood how greedy Ratcliffe was. They lowered their weapons too.

In desperation, Ratcliffe reached for a gun and fired at Powhatan. John Smith threw himself in front of the chief, and was shot instead.

The settlers were enraged. They grabbed Ratcliffe, and put him in chains.

Soon after, the settlers readied the *Susan Constant* to set sail for England. Thomas told Pocahontas that Smith would die if he stayed behind. "Going back is his only chance," Thomas explained.

Then Pocahontas approached Smith. She had a small pouch for him. It was filled with medicine from Grandmother Willow's bark. "It will help with the pain," she said.

Powhatan placed his own cloak over Smith.
"You are always welcome among our people,"
he said. "Thank you, my brother."

John Smith asked Pocahontas to go
with him to England. But when she
looked at the Indians sharing food with the
settlers, she knew that she had to stay.

She remembered her dream. And she realized what her path must be. She would continue working for peace between her people and the newcomers.

As Pocahontas watched the *Susan Constant* sail away, a gentle wind whispered in her ear. She knew that the same wind would carry John Smith safely home.